AGES
4+

MATH READINESS

edgeucational
publishing

NATIONAL
STANDARDS
COMPLIANT

MAKE IT FUN!

Dear Parent/Caregiver,

This book begins by reviewing numbers from zero to ten and then continuing with numbers from eleven to twenty. Then, addition and subtraction are introduced.

There are many fun and simple math activities you can do with your child:

- Ask your child if he or she wants his or her sandwich cut in two or four pieces (you can even use words like halves and fourths). He can also count out carrot sticks or any other food or snack (pickles, chips, etc…).

- Give your child small objects like beans, pennies, buttons, etc. to use for counting, adding, and subtracting.

- When walking with your child, ask questions such as, "How many people are sitting on the bench? How many flowerpots are on that porch?"

- Have your child count fingers and toes. Then ask him or her to count how many fingers and toes he or she has altogether. Use different combinations, such as how many eyes and fingers do you have altogether?

- Draw a picture with your child. Use specific numbers of objects in the illustration, such as "Let's draw two trees. Can you draw three birds in each tree?"

The more fun you make each activity, the more your child will benefit. This book provides you with a stepping stone in your child's education. You are an integral part of your child's ability to succeed. So, get started today and have fun!

COMPANION TO PROBLEM SOLVING

This book is a companion book for the Smart Alec Series Math Problem Solving book.

TABLE OF CONTENTS

Zero to Ten Review

Trace and write each number word and number.

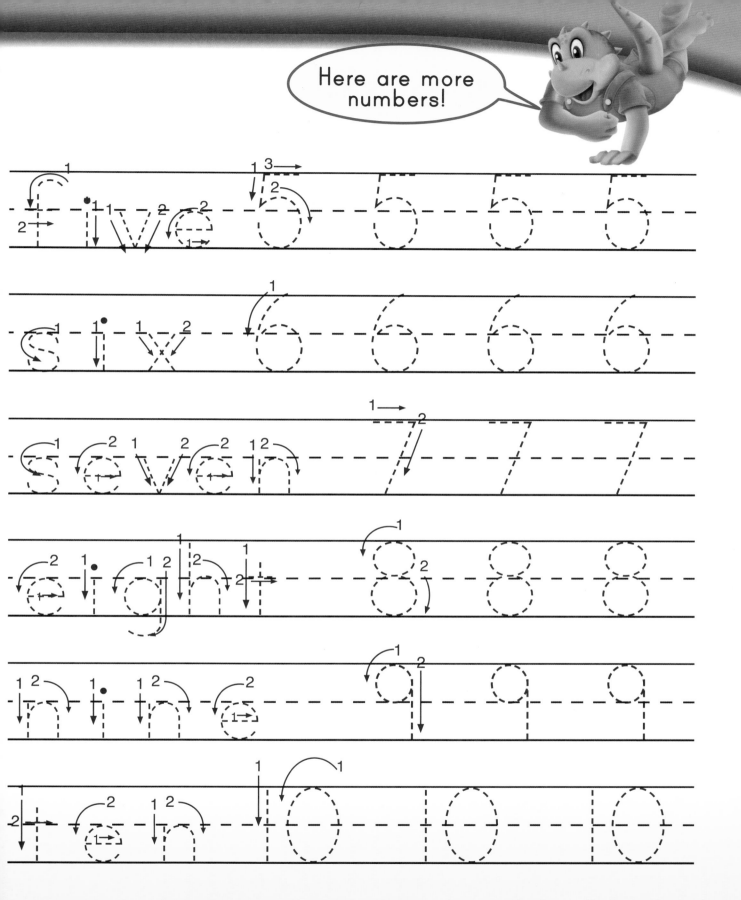

Here are more numbers!

Excellent Eleven

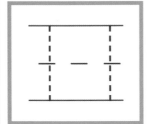

11
eleven

Trace the numbers.

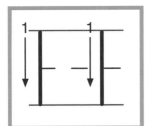 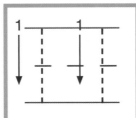

Write the number 11.

_____

_ _ _ _ _ _ _ _ _ _ _ _ _ _

_____

Count and write the number of ice cream cones.

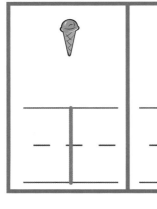    

Tremendous Twelve

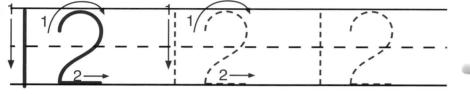

12 twelve

Trace the numbers.

Write the number 12.

_____

– – – – – – – – – – – – –

_____

Count. Write how many are in each box.

_____   _____

– – –   – – –

_____   _____

Excellent Thirteen

13
thirteen

Trace the numbers.

13 13 13 13 13

Write the number 13.

Fill in the missing numbers.

6	7	8	
10		12	

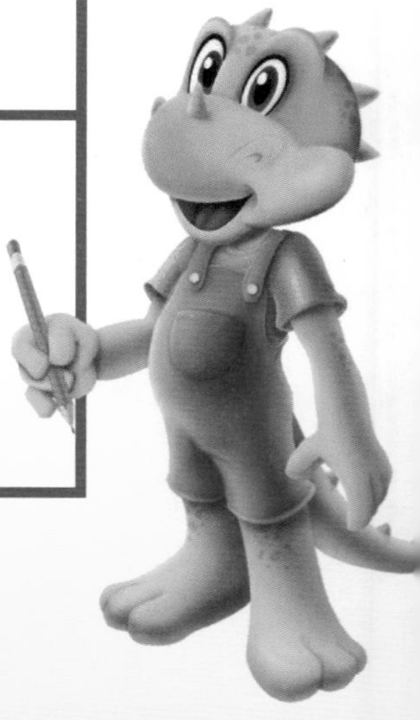

Fearless Fourteen

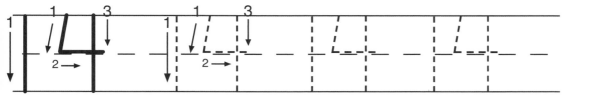

Trace the numbers.

Write the number 14.

Count and color 14 doughnuts.

Excellent Fifteen

Trace the numbers.

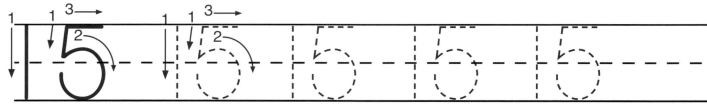

Write the number 15.

Count the marbles. Draw the missing marbles.

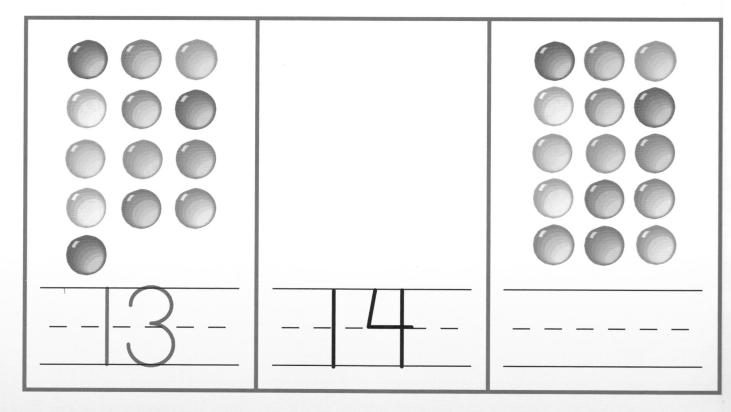

13

14

Superb Sixteen

16
sixteen

Trace the numbers.

16 16 16 16

Write the number 16.

Count. Circle the correct number below.

13 (16)   15 14   12 15

Super Seventeen

17
seventeen

Trace the numbers.

7 7 7 7 7 7 7 7

Write the number 17.

Draw a line to the matching pictures.

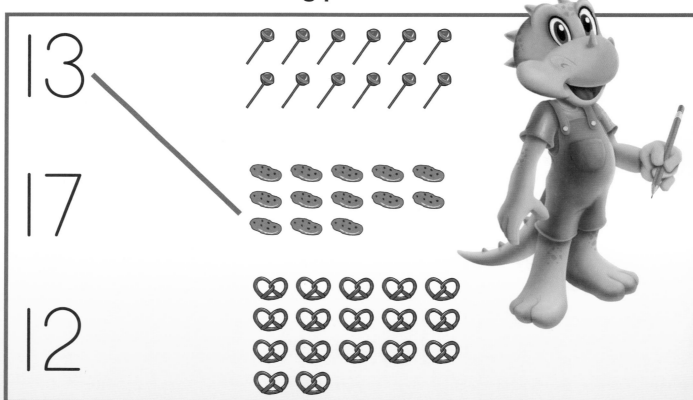

13

17

12

Extraordinary Eighteen

Trace the numbers.

Write the number 18.

- - - - - - - - - -

How many apples are in each tree?

How many apples are there in all?

Neat Nineteen

19
nineteen

Trace the numbers.

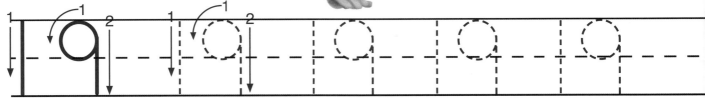

Write the number 19.

_____

_ _ _ _ _ _ _ _ _ _ _ _ _ _ _ _

_____

Count. Write the total number of fruits.

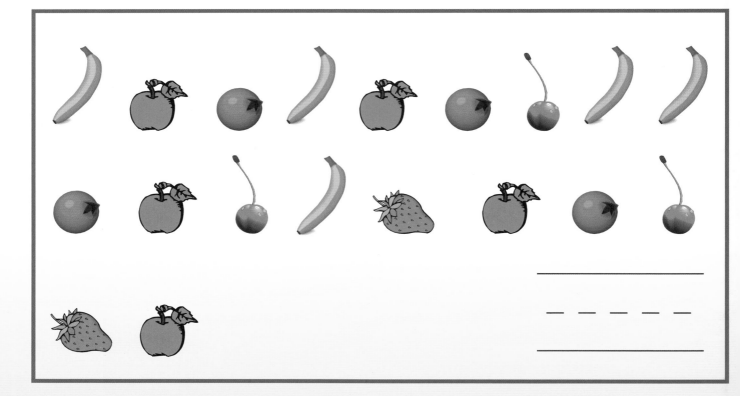

Marvelous Twenty

20 twenty

Trace the numbers.

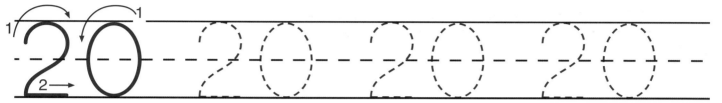

Write the number 20.

Count. Write the total number of vegetables.

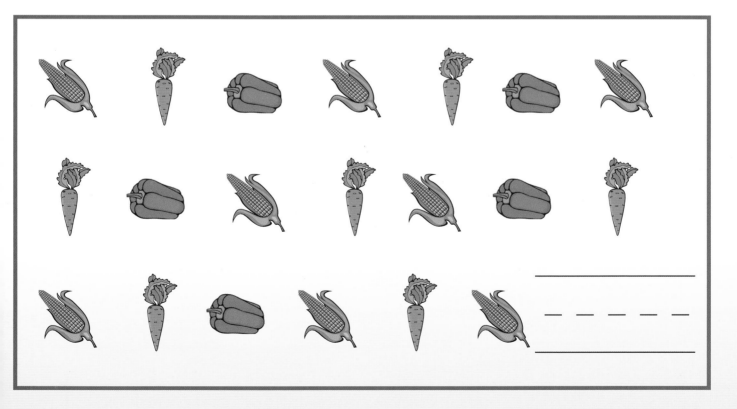

Missing Numbers

Fill in the missing numbers.

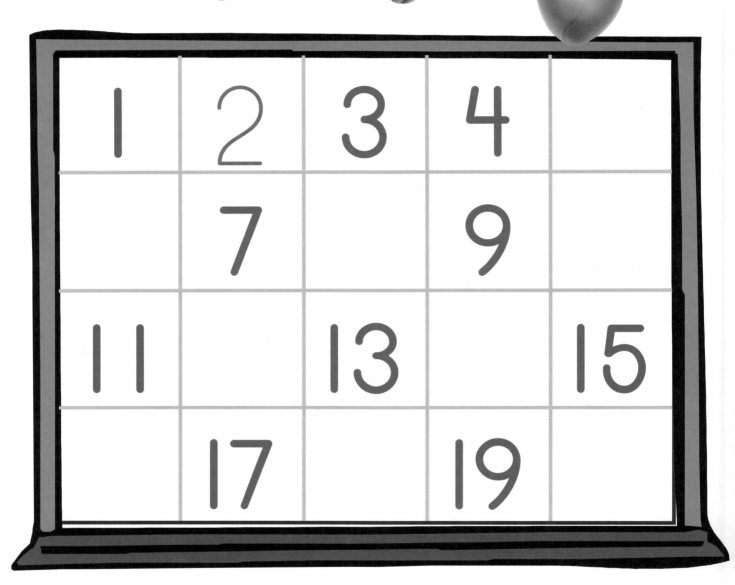

1	2	3	4	
	7		9	
11		13		15
	17		19	

Number Review

Circle the correct number.

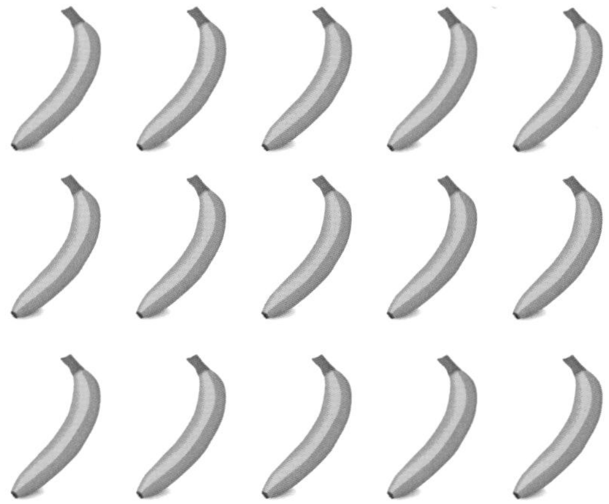

15 18

12 20

13 17

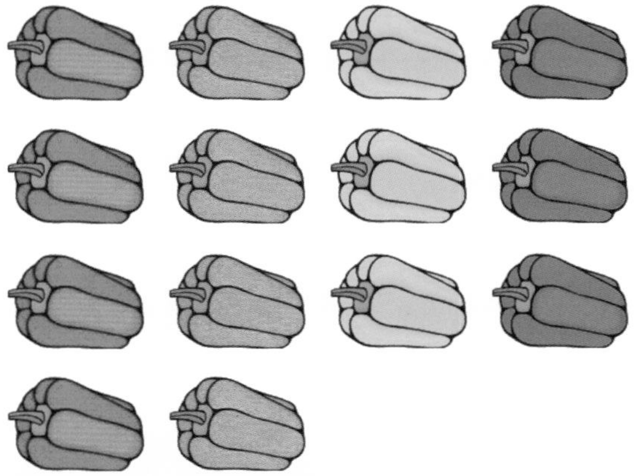

14 16

Vegetable Count

Write the number for each group
of vegetables.

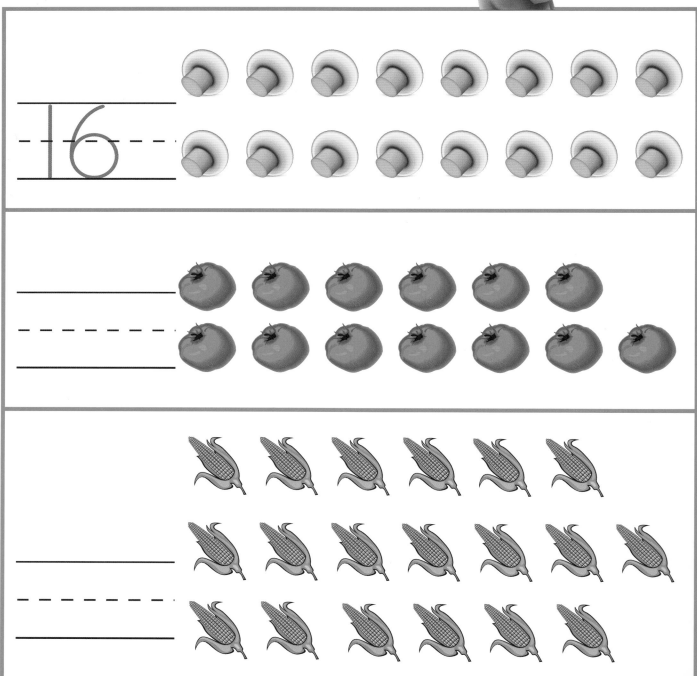

Fruit Count

Circle the correct number of fruits in each group.

18	
12	
14	
17	
13	

Addition

Adding is when we put together two or more groups, or sets.

Count the pictures below.
Write how many in all.

🍪 and 🍪🍪	is	3
🍌🍌 and 🍌🍌🍌	is	___
🥨🥨🥨🥨 and 🥨	is	___
🍒🍒 and 🍒🍒	is	___

Addition

This is an addition, or plus sign.   **+**

This is an equal sign.   **=**

🍓 **+** 🍓🍓🍓	**=**	4
🍦🍦 **+** 🍦	**=**	___
🍿🍿🍿 **+** 🍿🍿	**=**	___
🍪🍪🍪🍪 **+** 🍽	**=**	___

Adding On Zero

When you add 0 to a number,
the number stays the same.

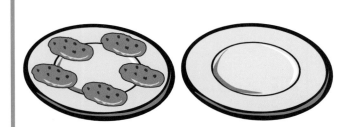

5 + 0 = 5

2 + 0 = ___

3 + 0 = ___

4 + 0 = ___

Adding On One

Add on 1 to each number.

$$1 + 1 = \underline{2}$$

$$4 + 1 = \underline{}$$

$$2 + 1 = \underline{}$$

$$0 + 1 = \underline{}$$

Adding On Two and Three

Add 2 or 3.

$1 + 2 =$ 3

$2 + 3 =$ _____

$1 + 3 =$ _____

$0 + 2 =$ _____

$2 + 2 =$ _____

Coloring Fun

Add and color.

5 = **blue**	**4** = **green**	**3** = **red**
2 = yellow	**1** = orange	**0** = **brown**

2+3=

4+0=

1+0=

2+1=

1+1=

2+3=

3+1=

2+2=

0+0=

Subtraction

Subtraction means to take away from a group or set. Put an X on the ice cream cones you take away.

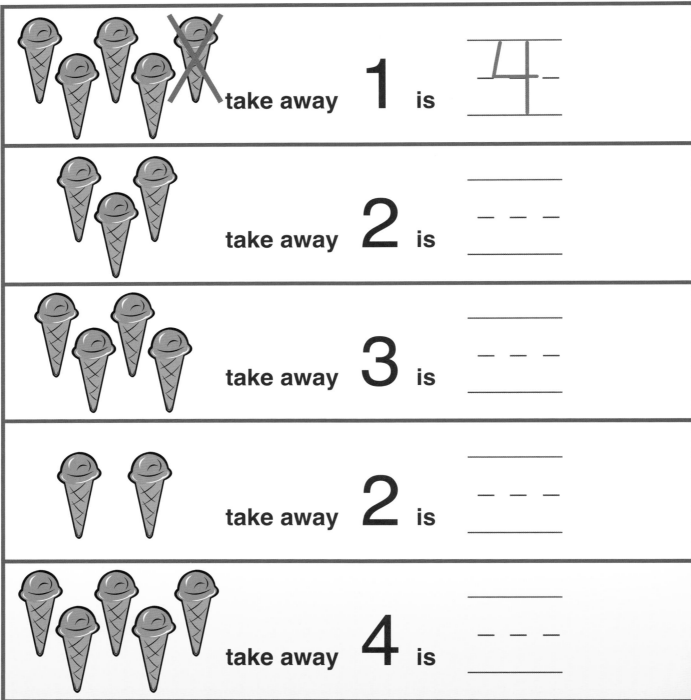

take away **1** is 4

take away **2** is ___

take away **3** is ___

take away **2** is ___

take away **4** is ___

Subtraction

Minus means to take away from a group or set.

This is a minus sign. —

This is an equal sign. =

Put an X on the objects you subtract.

 — 2 = 3

 — 1 = _____

 — 2 = _____

 — 0 = _____

Subtraction with Zero and One

When you take away zero from a number, the number stays the same. When you take away one, the number is one less.

Subtract 1 or 0.

4 – 1 =	3
3 – 0 =	_____
5 – 1 =	_____
2 – 0 =	_____
4 – 0 =	_____

Subtraction with Two and Three

Subtract 2 or 3.

$$5 - 2 = \underline{3}$$

$$4 - 3 = \underline{}$$

$$5 - 3 = \underline{}$$

$$3 - 3 = \underline{}$$

$$2 - 2 = \underline{}$$

$$3 - 2 = \underline{}$$

Subtraction Review

Subtract. Write the answers.

2 − 2 = 0	5 − 0 = ___
4 − 3 = ___	2 − 1 = ___
3 − 2 = ___	1 − 1 = ___
4 − 1 = ___	3 − 3 = ___
5 − 2 = ___	4 − 2 = ___
5 − 4 = ___	4 − 0 = ___

Addition and Subtraction

Add or subtract.

$4 - 1 =$ __3__	$2 + 3 =$ _ _ _
$1 + 3 =$ _ _ _	$0 + 1 =$ _ _ _
$3 - 2 =$ _ _ _	$5 - 1 =$ _ _ _
$2 + 1 =$ _ _ _	$4 - 2 =$ _ _ _
$3 - 3 =$ _ _ _	$5 - 4 =$ _ _ _
$4 + 0 =$ _ _ _	$1 + 1 =$ _ _ _

Fact Families

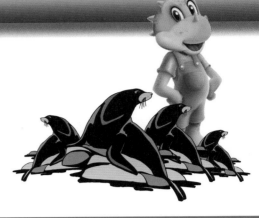

Addition and subtraction are related like people in a family.

$1 + 2 = \underline{3}$

$2 + 1 = \text{-----}$

$3 - 1 = \text{-----}$

$3 - 2 = \text{-----}$

$2 + 3 = \underline{5}$

$3 + 2 = \text{-----}$

$5 - 2 = \text{-----}$

$5 - 3 = \text{-----}$

$1 + 3 = \underline{4}$

$3 + 1 = \text{-----}$

$4 - 1 = \text{-----}$

$4 - 3 = \text{-----}$

Fact Family Fun

Use the pictures of the fact families to help you add and subtract.

2	🍒🍒
3	🍒🍒🍒
5	🍒🍒🍒🍒🍒

1	🍌
3	🍌🍌🍌
4	🍌🍌🍌🍌

$2 + 3 = 5$

$3 + 2 = $ _ _ _

$5 - 2 = 3$

$5 - 3 = $ _ _ _

$3 + 1 = $ _ _ _

$1 + 3 = $ _ _ _

$4 - 3 = $ _ _ _

$4 - 1 = $ _ _ _

Math Match

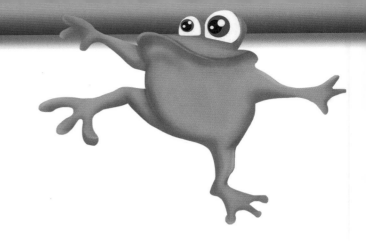

Match each number sentence to the correct picture.

1 + 3 = 4

2 + 1 = 3

2 + 2 = 4

1 + 1 = 2

0 + 1 = 1

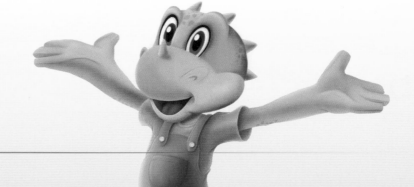

Addition Facts

Have an adult cut out the flash cards for you.
Use them to practice your addition facts.

0 + 1 =

0 + 2 =

0 + 3 =

0 + 4 =

0 + 5 =

1 + 1 =

1 + 2 =

1 + 3 =

1 + 4 =

2 + 1 =

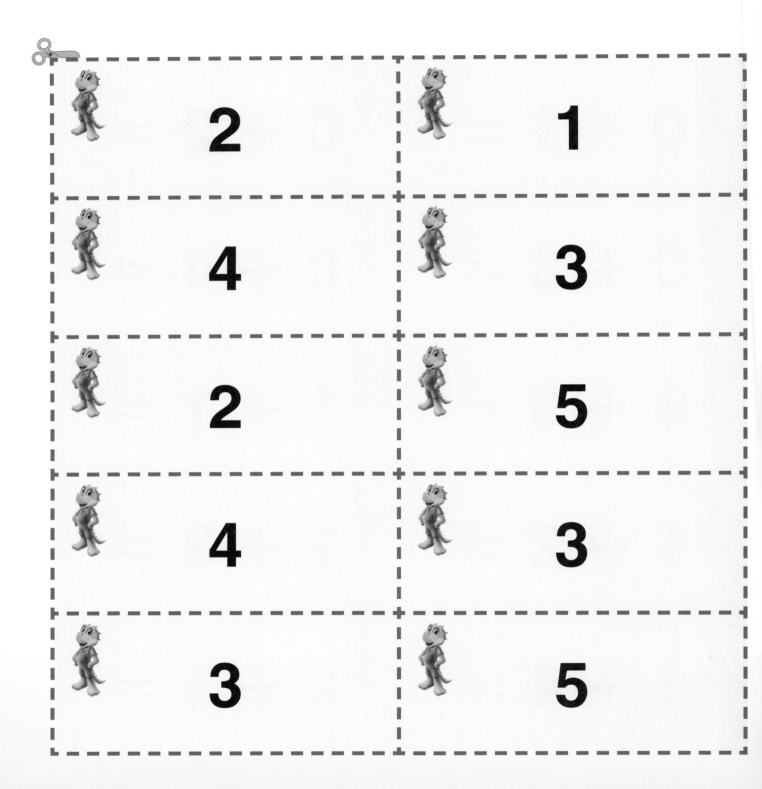

Subtraction Facts

Have an adult cut out the flash cards for you.
Use them to practice your subtraction facts.

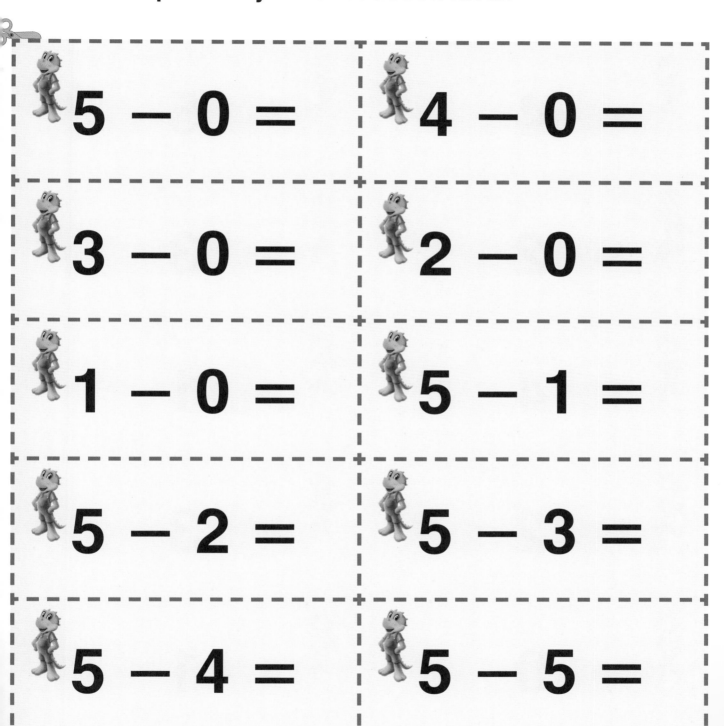

5 – 0 =

4 – 0 =

3 – 0 =

2 – 0 =

1 – 0 =

5 – 1 =

5 – 2 =

5 – 3 =

5 – 4 =

5 – 5 =

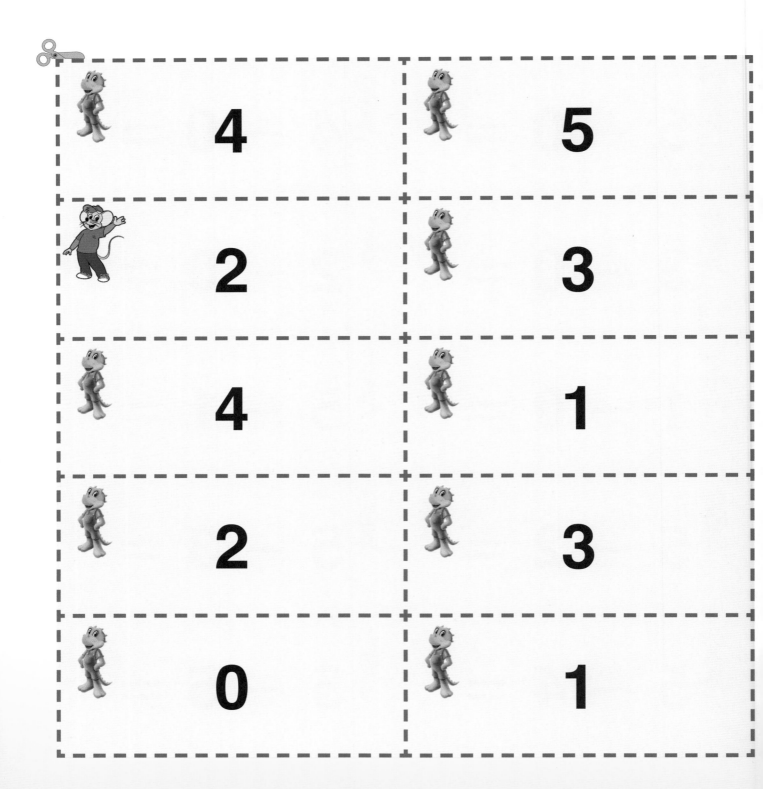

Fruit Count

Use the picture to help you answer the questions below.

1. How many apples are there?   — — —

2. How many oranges are there?   — — —

3. How many fruits are there in all?   — — —

4. If someone ate 3 apples, how many apples would be left?   — — —

Answer Key

Zero to Ten Review

Hi! I'm Smart Alec!

Trace and write each number word and number.

zero 0 0 0

one 1 1 1

two 2 2 2 2

three 3 3 3

four 4 4 4

Here are more numbers!

five 5 5 5 5

six 6 6 6 6

seven 7 7 7

eight 8 8 8

nine 9 9 9

ten 10 10 10

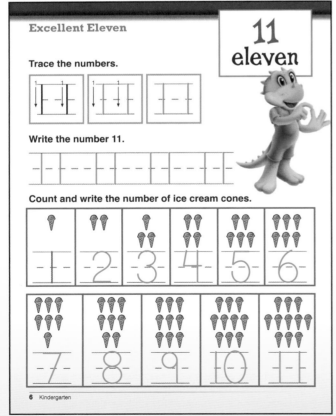

Excellent Eleven

11 eleven

Trace the numbers.

Write the number 11.

Count and write the number of ice cream cones.

1	2	3	4	5	6
7	8	9	10	11	

Tremendous Twelve

12 twelve

Trace the numbers.

12 12 12

Write the number 12.

12 12 12

Count. Write how many are in each box.

12   12

Excellent Thirteen

13 thirteen

Trace the numbers.

Write the number 13.

Fill in the missing numbers.

6	7	8	9
10	11	12	13

Fearless Fourteen

14 fourteen

Trace the numbers.

Write the number 14.

Count and color 14 doughnuts.

Excellent Fifteen

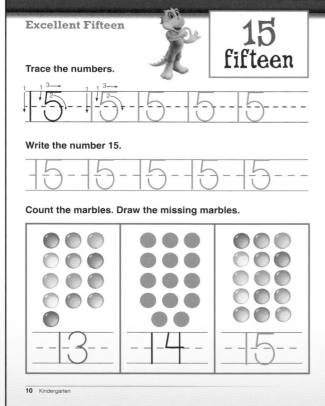

15 fifteen

Trace the numbers.

Write the number 15.

Count the marbles. Draw the missing marbles.

13   14   15

Superb Sixteen

16 sixteen

Trace the numbers.

Write the number 16.

Count. Circle the correct number below.

13 (16)   15 (14)   12 (15)

Super Seventeen

17 seventeen

Trace the numbers.

Write the number 17.

Draw a line to the matching pictures.

13

17

12

Extraordinary Eighteen

18 eighteen

Trace the numbers.

Write the number 18.

How many apples are in each tree?

How many apples are there in all?

Neat Nineteen

19 nineteen

Trace the numbers.

Write the number 19.

Count. Write the total number of fruits.

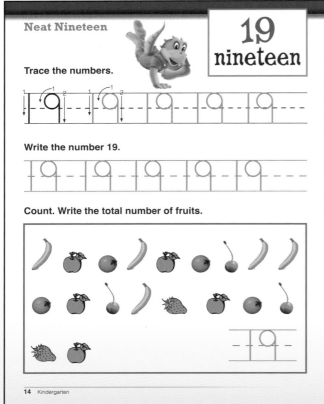

Marvelous Twenty

20 twenty

Trace the numbers.

Write the number 20.

Count. Write the total number of vegetables.

Missing Numbers

Fill in the missing numbers.

1	2	3	4	5
6	7	8	9	10
11	12	13	14	15
16	17	18	19	20

1 2 3 4 5 6 7 8 9 10 11 12 13 14 15 16 17 18 19 20

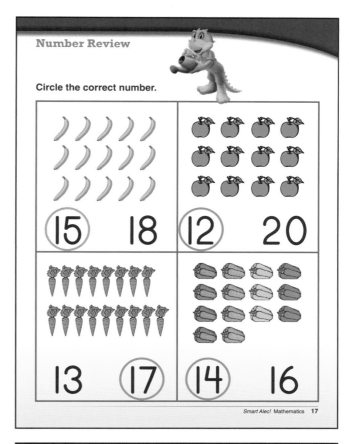

Number Review

Circle the correct number.

(15)   18

(12)   20

13   (17)

(14)   16

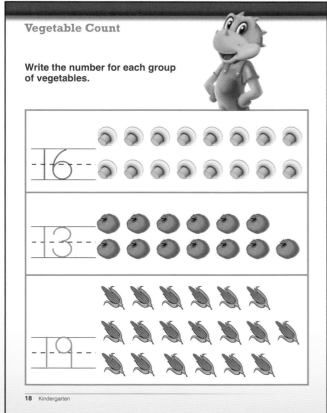

Vegetable Count

Write the number for each group of vegetables.

16

13

19

Fruit Count

Circle the correct number of fruits in each group.

18

12

14

17

13

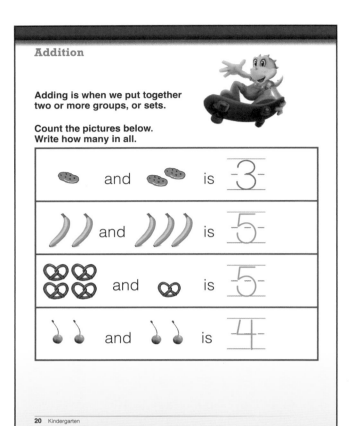

Addition

Adding is when we put together
two or more groups, or sets.

Count the pictures below.
Write how many in all.

🍪 and 🍪🍪	is	3
))) and))))	is	5
🥨🥨🥨🥨 and 🥨	is	5
🍒🍒 and 🍒🍒	is	4

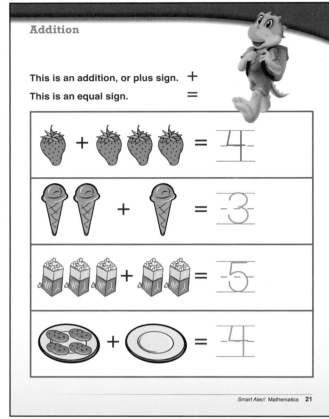

Addition

This is an addition, or plus sign. +

This is an equal sign. =

🍓 + 🍓🍓🍓	=	4
🍦🍦 + 🍦	=	3
🍿🍿🍿 + 🍿🍿	=	5
🍪🍪🍪 + ⬭	=	4

Adding On Zero

When you add 0 to a number,
the number stays the same.

$$5 + 0 = 5$$

$$2 + 0 = 2$$

$$3 + 0 = 3$$

$$4 + 0 = 4$$

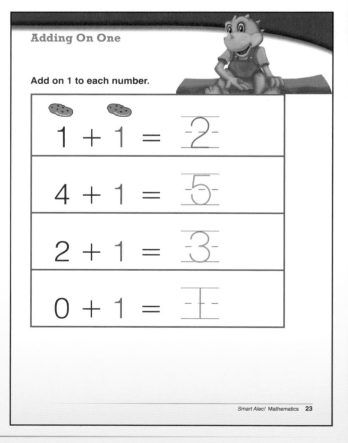

Adding On One

Add on 1 to each number.

$$1 + 1 = 2$$

$$4 + 1 = 5$$

$$2 + 1 = 3$$

$$0 + 1 = 1$$

Adding On Two and Three

Add 2 or 3.

$1 + 2 = 3$

$2 + 3 = 5$

$1 + 3 = 4$

$0 + 2 = 2$

$2 + 2 = 4$

Coloring Fun

Add and color.

5 = blue	4 = green	3 = red
2 = yellow	1 = orange	0 = brown

Subtraction

Subtraction means to take away from a group or set. Put an X on the ice cream cones you take away.

take away 1 is 4

take away 2 is ___

take away 3 is ___

take away 2 is 0

take away 4 is ___

Subtraction

Minus means to take away from a group or set.

This is a minus sign. —

This is an equal sign. =

Put an X on the objects you subtract.

$- 2 = 3$

$- 1 = 3$

$- 2 = 1$

$- 0 = 2$

Subtraction with Zero and One

When you take away zero from a number, the number stays the same. When you take away one, the number is one less.

Subtract 1 or 0.

4 − 1 =	3
3 − 0 =	3
5 − 1 =	4
2 − 0 =	2
4 − 0 =	4

Subtraction with Two and Three

Subtract 2 or 3.

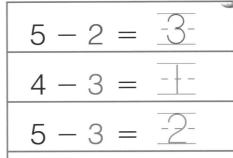

5 − 2 =	3
4 − 3 =	1
5 − 3 =	2
3 − 3 =	0
2 − 2 =	0
3 − 2 =	1

Subtraction Review

Subtract. Write the answers.

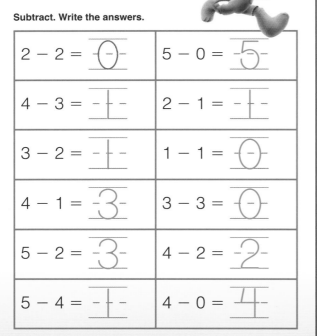

2 − 2 = 0	5 − 0 = 5
4 − 3 = 1	2 − 1 = 1
3 − 2 = 1	1 − 1 = 0
4 − 1 = 3	3 − 3 = 0
5 − 2 = 3	4 − 2 = 2
5 − 4 = 1	4 − 0 = 4

Addition and Subtraction

Add or subtract.

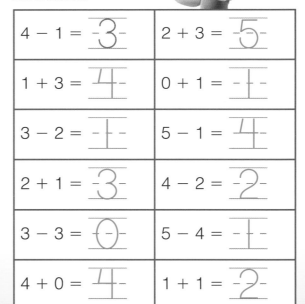

4 − 1 = 3	2 + 3 = 5
1 + 3 = 4	0 + 1 = 1
3 − 2 = 1	5 − 1 = 4
2 + 1 = 3	4 − 2 = 2
3 − 3 = 0	5 − 4 = 1
4 + 0 = 4	1 + 1 = 2

Fact Families

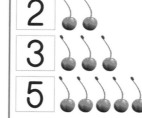

Addition and subtraction are related like people in a family.

1 + 2 = 3
2 + 1 = 3
3 − 1 = 2
3 − 2 = 1

2 + 3 = 5
3 + 2 = 5
5 − 2 = 3
5 − 3 = 2

1 + 3 = 4
3 + 1 = 4
4 − 1 = 3
4 − 3 = 1

Fact Family Fun

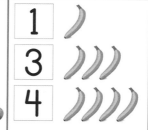

Use the pictures of the fact families to help you add and subtract.

2
3
5

1
3
4

2 + 3 = 5
3 + 2 = 5
5 − 2 = 3
5 − 3 = 2

3 + 1 = 4
1 + 3 = 4
4 − 3 = 1
4 − 1 = 3

Math Match

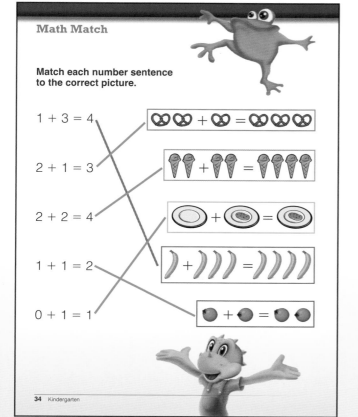

Match each number sentence to the correct picture.

1 + 3 = 4

2 + 1 = 3

2 + 2 = 4

1 + 1 = 2

0 + 1 = 1

Addition Facts

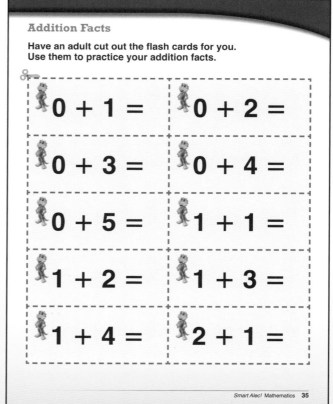

Have an adult cut out the flash cards for you.
Use them to practice your addition facts.

0 + 1 =	0 + 2 =
0 + 3 =	0 + 4 =
0 + 5 =	1 + 1 =
1 + 2 =	1 + 3 =
1 + 4 =	2 + 1 =

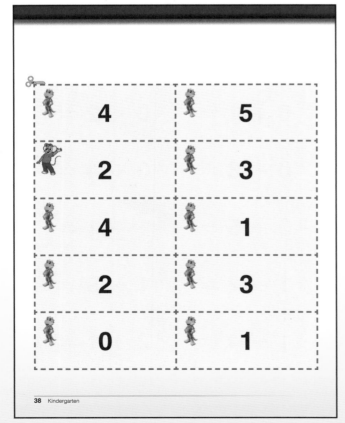

2	1
4	3
2	5
4	3
3	5

Subtraction Facts

**Have an adult cut out the flash cards for you.
Use them to practice your subtraction facts.**

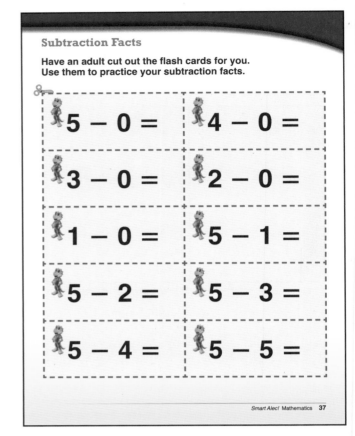

$5 - 0 =$	$4 - 0 =$
$3 - 0 =$	$2 - 0 =$
$1 - 0 =$	$5 - 1 =$
$5 - 2 =$	$5 - 3 =$
$5 - 4 =$	$5 - 5 =$

4	5
2	3
4	1
2	3
0	1

Fruit Count

**Use the picture to help you answer
the questions below.**

1. How many apples are there? 3

2. How many oranges are there? 2

3. How many fruits in all? 5

4. If someone ate 3 apples, how
   many apples would be left? 0